LEAVE, BEES!

A Thai Folk Tale

Based on a story by
Margaret Read MacDonald,
Supaporn Vathanaprida, and Wajuppa Tossa

Illustrated by Amanda Hall

HAMPTON-BROWN

Characters

Raja and
the other elephants

Ranee and
the other bees

What happens when the big elephants and the little bees help each other?

LEAVE, BEES!

Raja and the other elephants are walking in the forest.

They smell smoke. They see a fire!

"Oh, no! Run!" shouts Raja. "We must get away!"

Song

Run!

Run, run, run!
Run away! Run away!

Run from the fire!
Go THIS way.
Go THAT way.

Run, run, RUN!

The elephants do not know where to go. The fire is coming quickly! The elephants are afraid.

Then they see some bees. “Can you help us?” Raja asks the bees. “Is there a safe place to go?”

Ranee stops. She says, "We will help you now, if you will help us later."

"Yes, we promise!" all of the elephants shout at once.

The bees fly high into the smoky sky. They look around.

Is there fire
in the east?
Yes!

Is there fire
in the west?
Yes!

Is there fire
in the north?
Yes!

Is there fire
in the south?
NO!

Ranee flies back to the elephants. She says, "Go south to the river!"

The elephants follow Ranee. They run and run. Finally, they get to the river.

"Now you must help us!" says Ranee. "We do not like the smoke. We want to hide in your noses."

The elephants do not want bees in their noses! But they open their mouths. The bees fly all the way inside and into the elephants' noses.

Ranee says to the elephants, "Now go in the water. Do not move!"

The elephants go in the water and wait. The bees wait in the elephants' noses. They are all safe!

The bees are happy.

The elephants are not happy! The bees tickle their noses. The bees buzz inside the elephants' heads. But the elephants keep their mouths closed to protect the bees.

The fire burns down one hill. It burns up another hill.

Finally, the fire is gone.

The elephants open their mouths.

"Bees, come out now! It is safe outside!" the elephants say.

Ranee peeks out. She says, "We do not want to come out. We like this warm, dark place." Then she goes back inside.

The elephants are worried. They want the bees out of their noses! What can they do?

Song

Little Bees

Will you please come out?
Will you please fly away?
Little bees, little bees,
You cannot stay!

Are you leaving soon?
Can you find a new home?
Little bees, little bees,
Please leave us alone!

The bees will not leave. Finally, Raja tells the elephants, "Blow water through your noses!"

The elephants blow.

And they blow.

And they blow!

The elephants blow so hard that their noses grow! But the bees are still inside.

Raja thinks. Then he says, "The bees do not like smoke. We can use smoke to get them out."

"Yes! Yes!" the elephants cheer.

Raja makes a fire. The elephants let the smoke fill their long noses.

The bees shoot from the elephants' smoky noses! Then the bees hurry to find a new home.

The elephants are happy now.
They like their new noses, too!

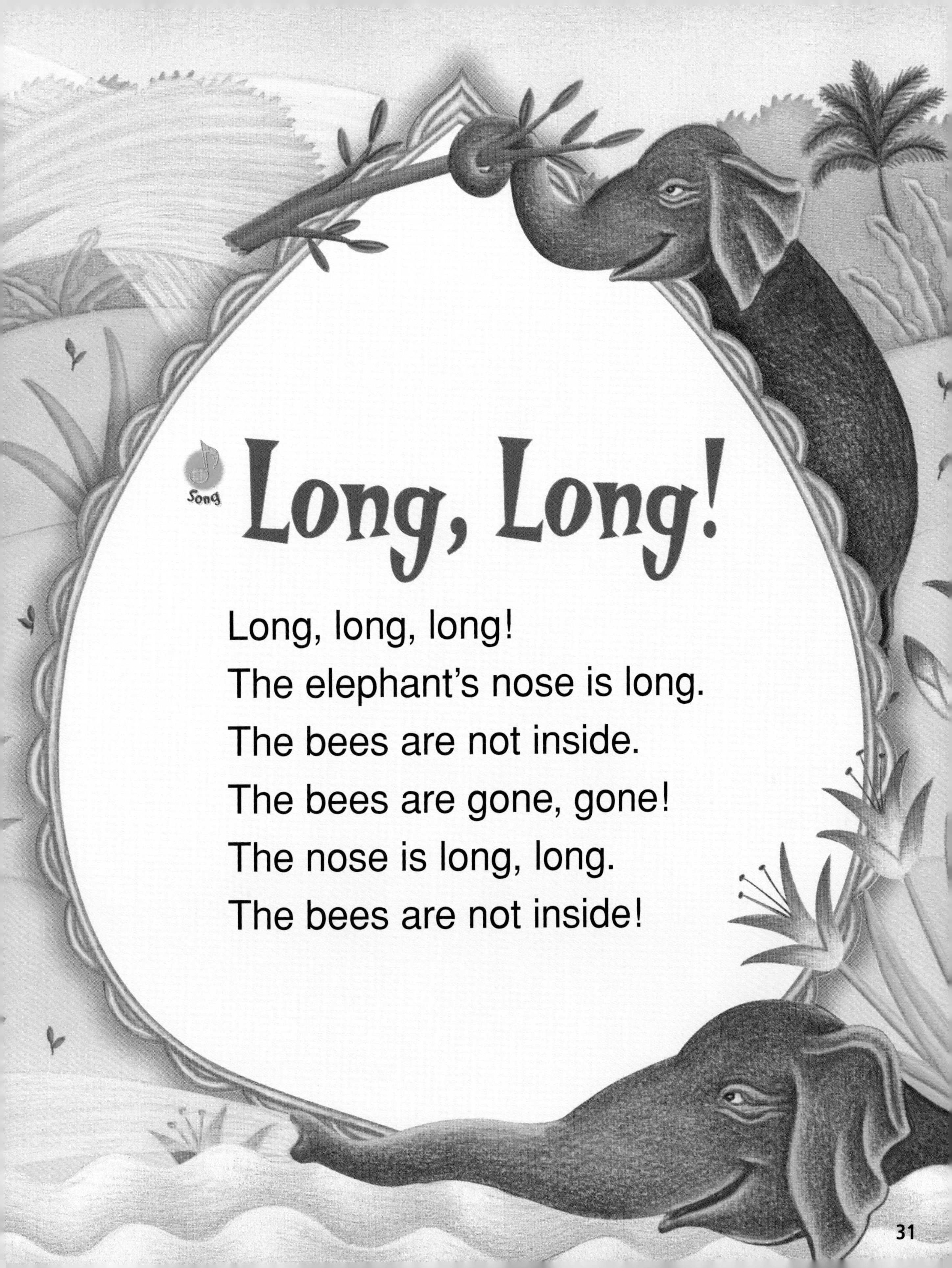

Song

Long, Long!

Long, long, long!
The elephant's nose is long.
The bees are not inside.
The bees are gone, gone!
The nose is long, long.
The bees are not inside!

Today, elephants still like to blow water through their long noses. And bees stay out of the way!